The Crown

Kasia Reay

Illustrated by Clara Booth

Schofield&Sims

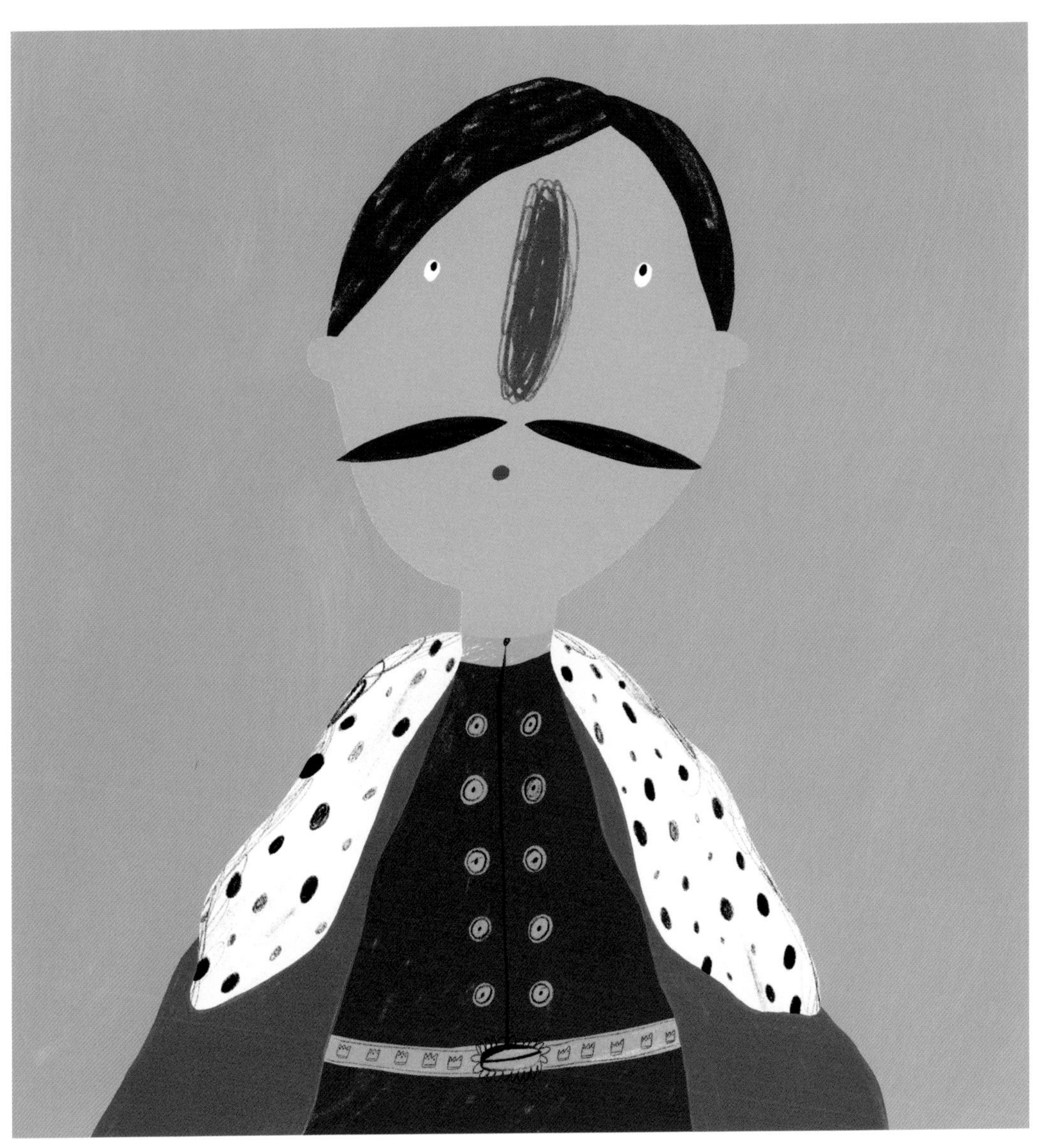

A week ago, the king lost his crown. "I like my crown so much! I must have a crown!" he said.

He was so sad. "I feel like a painter with no paint or a cook with no pans," he said.

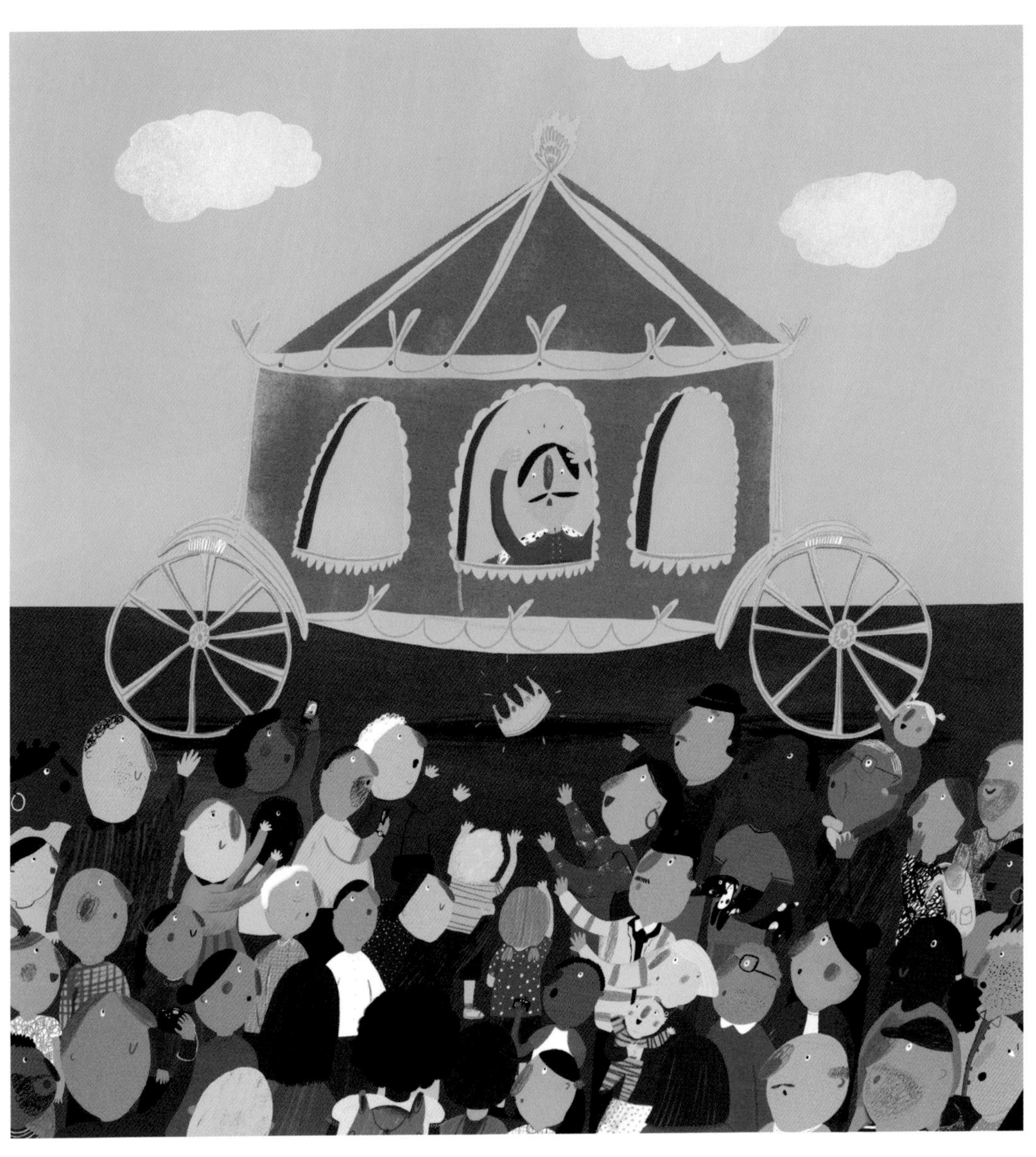

He had a think. Did he drop his crown in a crowd in town?

Did it land in a litter bin down the road?

Did his crown slip into the moat from his boat?

Did it sink and turn into a swing for the fish?

Did he lend his crown to an owl to have as a nest?

Did he lend his crown to a clown to dress up like a king...

or did the crown just vanish into thin air?

"I feel so sad," the king said to the queen. Tears fell onto his cheeks.

"Stop weeping and have a look under this cloak," said the queen with a grin.

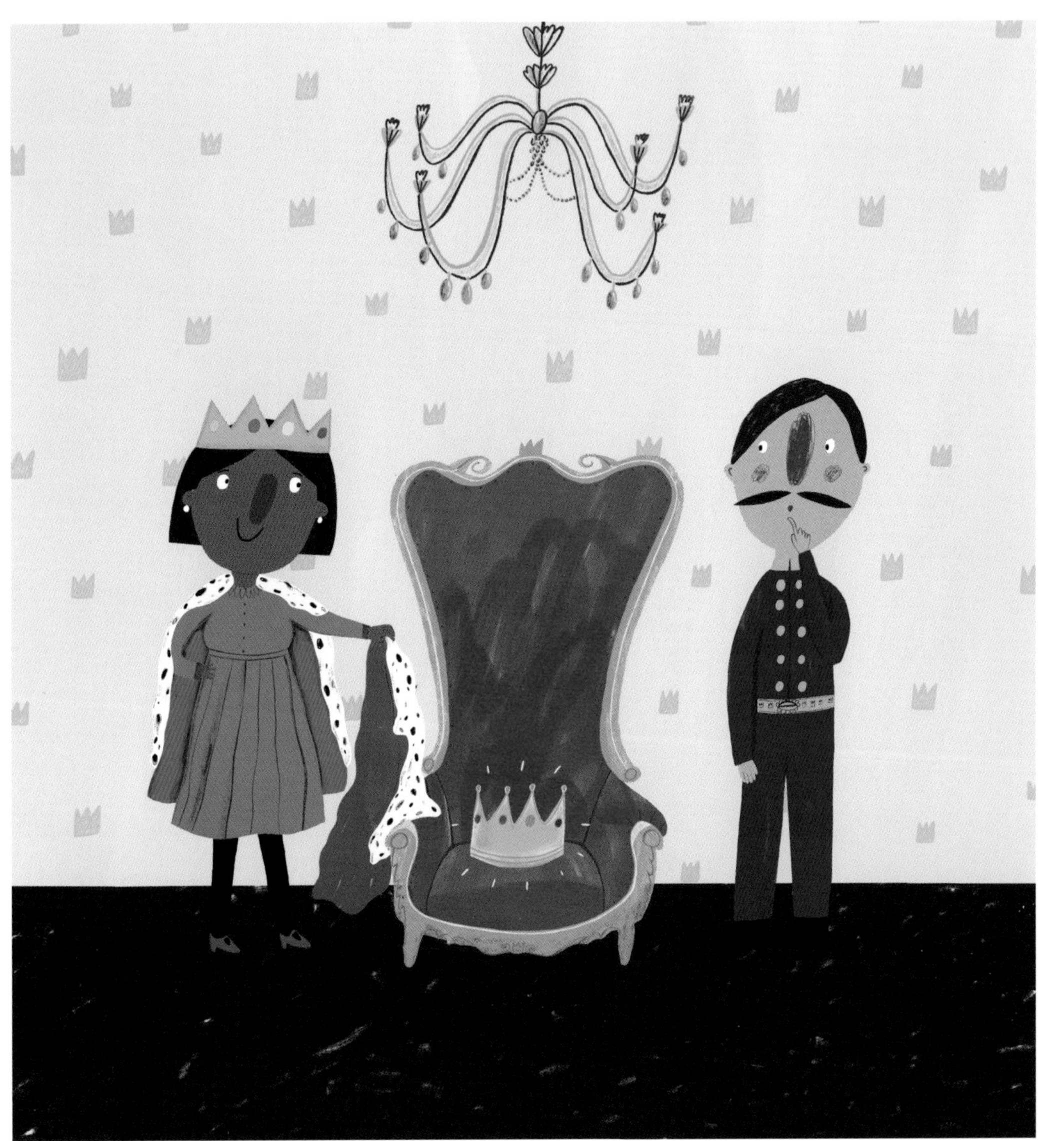

Marco N

He's a joker w
messing abou
always means
if he sometim
things wrong.

Waxy Max

He's very sporty and football mad. On the outside, he's tough, but underneath he's got the biggest heart.

Philippa Feltpen

A real peacemaker, she helps keep the other Pens in order by sorting out arguments and giving good advice.

Are you feeling brave, Splodge, 'cause we're going camping!

Squiggle and Splodge

The Scribble twins! They're both quiet, both shy. Although they may not look alike, they do almost everything together.

Enter ...

Squiggle, what do you think of my cape?
I like it. You look very heroic!

Pens

Helping you to get to know God more

God's Heroes

Written by
Alexa Tewkesbury

Every day a short Bible reading is brought to life with the help of the Pens characters. A related question and prayer apply this to daily life. Written in four sections, two focusing on the lives of Pens and two on Bible characters, young children will be inspired to learn more of God and His Word.

What's inside?

CWR

Day 1 THE GREAT ADVENTURE

'... fill your minds with those things that are good ... true, noble, right, pure, lovely, and honourable.' (Philippians 4 v 8)

Pens-the-Adventurers

Pens were going camping in Philippa's garden – for one exciting night.

We're camping adventurers!

'We're camping explorers!' shrieked Charlotte and Denzil.

'We're camping heroes!' squealed Squiggle and Splodge.

Gloria just grumbled, 'My bag's not big enough!'

She was trying to pack too many hats. She wanted a sun hat in case it was sunny, a rain hat in case it was wet, and a night hat in case she was cold in bed.

'We're going camping for the first time ever,' Charlotte smiled. 'This is our BIGGEST adventure yet! Don't waste time being grumpy.'

God's heroes want to make the most of their adventure with Him.

Who would you like to go camping with?

Pens Prayer

Father, thank You for fun adventures like camping. Help me to include You in all my adventures. Amen.

The Great Adventure

'... look out for one another's interests, not just for your own.' (Philippians 2 v 4)

Troublesome Tent

Pens were putting up their tents in Philippa's garden.

Denzil, Max, Sharpy and Marco's was round and orange, and they put it up easily. Charlotte, Gloria, Squiggle and Splodge's was square-shaped and blue – and they couldn't put it up at all.

'Why is this tent so difficult?' moaned Gloria. 'I don't even like the colour. I wish ours was round and orange and easy, too.'

'I'll help you,' said Philippa.

'We'll *all* help you,' added Denzil. 'That's what GREAT CAMPING HEROES do! Don't worry, Gloria. We promise we won't leave you without a tent to sleep in.'

God's heroes need to be ready to help others whenever they can.

If you went camping, what would you need to take with you?

Pens Prayer

Dear Lord God, please help me to be ready to help others whenever I can. Amen.

Day 3 The Great Adventure

'But you, O LORD … restore my courage.' (Psalm 3 v 3)

Gloria plays football

Pens were gazing proudly at their tents.

We did it!
We even put up the troublesome tent.

Of course, we did. We're GREAT CAMPING HEROES!

'What shall we do now?' asked Charlotte.

'We could play football,' suggested Max.

'Good idea,' replied Philippa. 'Just be careful the ball doesn't go in my flowerbeds.'

Gloria was doubtful. 'I've never played football before,' she frowned. 'I might not be able to.'

'It's easy,' smiled Denzil. 'We'll all show you how. Besides, this is an adventure. Be brave! It's the perfect time to try something new.'

God's heroes know He will be with them when they need to be brave.

When might you need to ask God to help you be brave?

Pens Prayer

Heavenly Lord, thank You that You are always there and You can help me to be brave. Amen.

Day 4 The Great Adventure

'... he gives you food and fills your hearts with happiness.' (Acts 14 v 17)

Wild supper

Food Adventure

Food Adventure

Pens were looking for Sharpy.

'Where is he?' wondered Splodge.

'Found him!' called Squiggle.

Sharpy was in the round, orange tent. His ears were pricked. His tongue was hanging out – and his nose was snuffling in Pens' basket of food!

'Poor Sharpy!' laughed Max. 'We spent so long playing football, we forgot about supper. His tummy must be empty.'

Marco unpacked the camping stove. Soon Pens were cooking soup which they ate with crusty bread from Philippa's kitchen.

'Delicious!' grinned Charlotte.

'All the more so,' added Max, 'because we're eating outside in the wild!'

God's heroes trust Him to feed them when they're hungry.

What different flavours of soup can you think of? Do you have a favourite?

Pens Prayer

Inside or outside, at home or away, thank You, Father God, for giving me food to eat. Amen.

Day 5 The Great Adventure

'My devoted servant, with whom I am pleased ...' (Isaiah 53 v 11)

Story-tellers

Pens were sitting on the grass.

'It's getting dark,' remarked Philippa.

'We can't go to bed yet,' said Denzil. 'We're far too wide awake.'

'What shall we do?' asked Max. 'I'm too full of soup to play football again.'

'Let's tell each other stories,' suggested Gloria.

So the great Pens storytelling time began.

They told stories of good Pens, bad Pens, clever Pens and brave Pens.

Then Charlotte told a story about Jesus; how He touched a blind man's eyes and the man could see again.

'The man cried, "Thank You, Jesus!",' smiled Charlotte. '"You're my HERO!"'

Jesus is the greatest hero in the Bible. He ALWAYS put God and other people before Himself.

Do you know what we call the amazing things Jesus did with God's power?

Pens Prayer

Lord God, I want to grow up like Jesus – self-LESS not self-ISH. Amen.

Day 6 The Great Adventure

'Jesus answered them, "Have faith in God."' (Mark 11 v 22)

Philippa's bathroom

Pens were getting ready for bed.

They rolled out their sleeping bags.

They plumped up their pillows.

Suddenly Splodge said, ‘But where are we going to brush our teeth?’

‘Simple,’ replied Philippa. ‘You can all come and use my bathroom.’

Splodge couldn’t help frowning.

‘What’s wrong?’ asked Philippa.

‘It’s just,’ Splodge began, ‘if we’re supposed to be GREAT CAMPING HEROES, is it really all right to borrow someone’s bathroom?’

‘Of course,’ smiled Philippa. ‘Heroes need a bit of help sometimes. Even Bible heroes. They trusted God and He looked after them.’

God’s heroes rely on His help, and God LOVES to help them.

When do you brush your teeth?

Pens Prayer

Thank You, loving God, that I can always ask You for help when I need it. Amen.

Day 7 The Great Adventure

'As I lie in bed, I remember you …' (Psalm 63 v 6)

Noisy night

Pens were snuggled up in their sleeping bags.

I'm *still* wide awake.

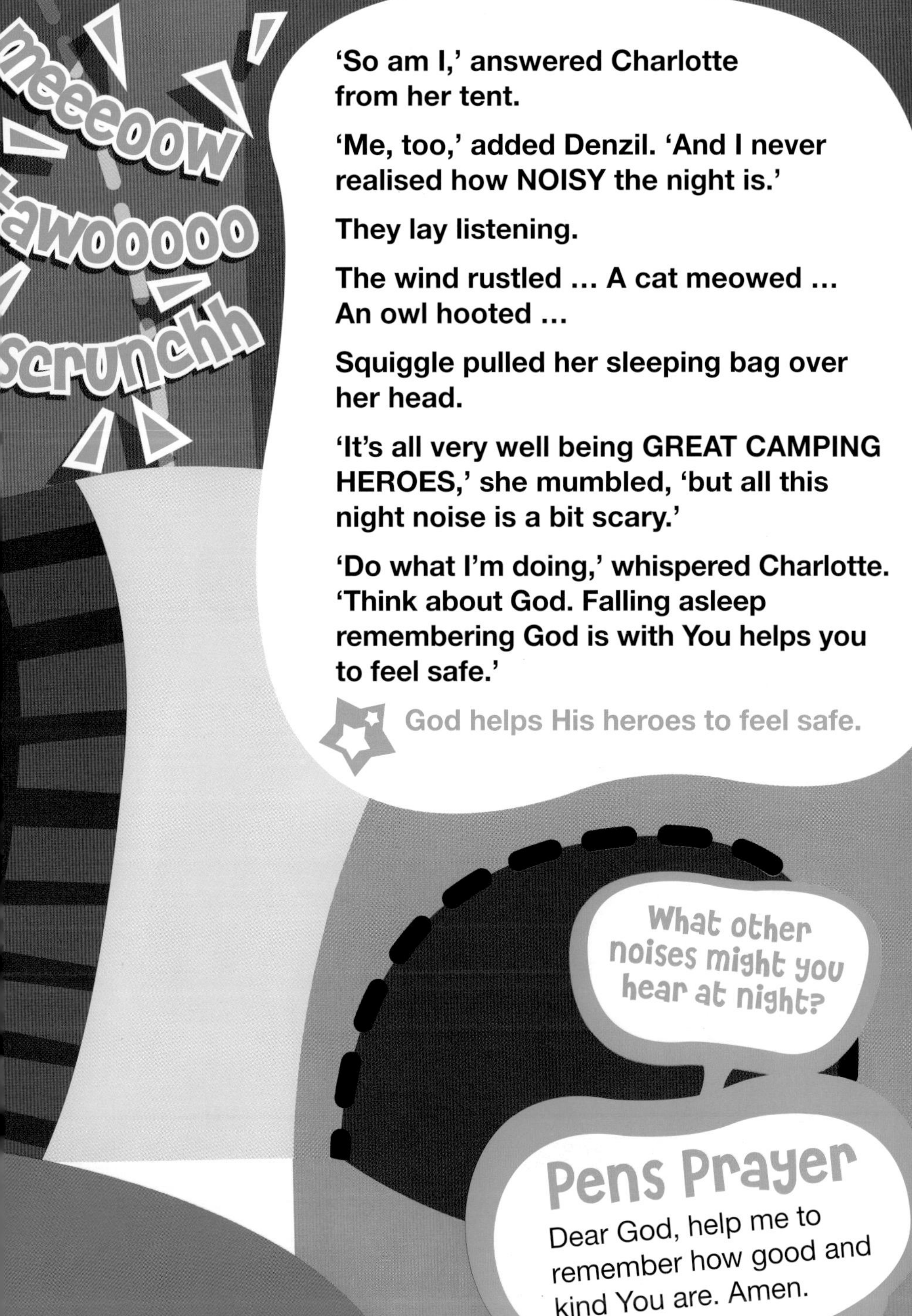

'So am I,' answered Charlotte from her tent.

'Me, too,' added Denzil. 'And I never realised how NOISY the night is.'

They lay listening.

The wind rustled … A cat meowed … An owl hooted …

Squiggle pulled her sleeping bag over her head.

'It's all very well being GREAT CAMPING HEROES,' she mumbled, 'but all this night noise is a bit scary.'

'Do what I'm doing,' whispered Charlotte. 'Think about God. Falling asleep remembering God is with You helps you to feel safe.'

God helps His heroes to feel safe.

What other noises might you hear at night?

Pens Prayer

Dear God, help me to remember how good and kind You are. Amen.

Day 8 The Great Adventure

'Whenever I am anxious and worried, you comfort me and make me glad.' (Psalm 94 v 19)

Wet

Pens were sleeping. Suddenly –

Pit-pat-plop ...

More noises in the night.

What's that?

Just rain. But we're
dry in our tent.
Go back to sleep.

Drip-drap-drop …

'*Our* tent's not dry,' muttered Max, 'There's rain dripping on my sleeping bag!'

Sharpy shook his head as water trickled into his ear.

'We might be GREAT CAMPING HEROES,' groaned Marco and Denzil, 'but we'll never get to sleep in a leaky tent.'

Max smiled an encouraging smile. 'No point being grumpy,' he said. 'Let's be REAL HEROES and work out what to do …'

God will always encourage His heroes when the adventure with Him seems difficult.

Do you know how God 'encourages' us?

Pens Prayer

Lord, thank You for encouraging me. I never want to give up on my adventure with You. Amen.

Day 9
The Great Adventure
'Trust in the LORD for ever; he will always protect us.' (Isaiah 26 v 4)
Dry

Pens were awake.

'Good morning!' chirped Charlotte.

'Lovely sleep!' beamed Gloria.

'Best ever!' chuckled Squiggle and Splodge.

They got up and went to visit Denzil, Max, Sharpy and Marco in the other tent – but it was empty.

'Their sleeping bags have gone, too,' frowned Charlotte.

Splodge looked very worried. 'I hope,' she mumbled, 'they haven't been eaten by a GREAT PENS-EATING MONSTER!'

'We haven't been eaten by anything!' laughed a voice.

It was Denzil. He was peeping out of Philippa's garden shed.

'Our tent was leaking so we slept in here. Snuggly and dry we kept, too!'

God's heroes trust He'll help them find ways to sort out their problems.

Pens Prayer

Thank You, dear God, for listening to my prayers and for helping me in so many different ways. Amen.

Do you need to ask God to help you with a problem today?

Day 10 The Great Adventure

'I am the LORD your God; I strengthen you and say, "Do not be afraid; I will help you."' (Isaiah 41 v 13)

Pens were packing up.

First they took down the square, blue tent. Then they took down the round, orange one.

When everything was tucked into bags, Philippa brought out hot toast and marmalade for breakfast.

'I love camping!' cried Squiggle.

'So do I!' giggled Splodge.

'It is actually rather fun,' agreed Gloria.

'We've been GREAT CAMPING HEROES!' cheered Marco. 'We trusted God to take care of us and we looked after each other, too.'

'AND,' added Max, 'we didn't give up – not even when our tent was leaky!'

Charlotte chuckled excitedly, 'It's been brilliant! I *love* being a hero.'

The more God's heroes trust in Him, the stronger they become.

How would you like to spend a holiday?

Pens Prayer

Father God, I praise You that when I trust in You, You help me do amazing things! Amen.

MOSES, A HERO FOR GOD

The fire in the bush

Day 11

'... the LORD appeared [to Moses] as a flame coming from the middle of a bush.' (Exodus 3 v 2)

Moses was a shepherd.

'I'm a very ordinary man,' he thought, 'doing very ordinary things.'

One day he was looking after the sheep and goats when suddenly –

'That bush is on fire!' he cried.

But the fire wasn't burning the bush. The flames just flickered and danced among the leaves.

Moses stared and stared. 'How can a bush be on fire without burning?' he wondered.

Then he heard it. A voice! It came from deep inside the flames – and it was calling his name!

'Moses! Moses!'

Moses felt very ordinary, but God wanted him to do something special.

We use the milk from sheep and goats. Which other animal's milk do we use?

Pens Prayer

Thank You, Lord God, that no one is 'ordinary' in Your eyes. To You we are all SUPER-SPECIAL! Amen.

Moses, a Hero for God

The fire in the bush

Day 12

'Take off your sandals, because you are standing on holy ground.' (Exodus 3 v 5)

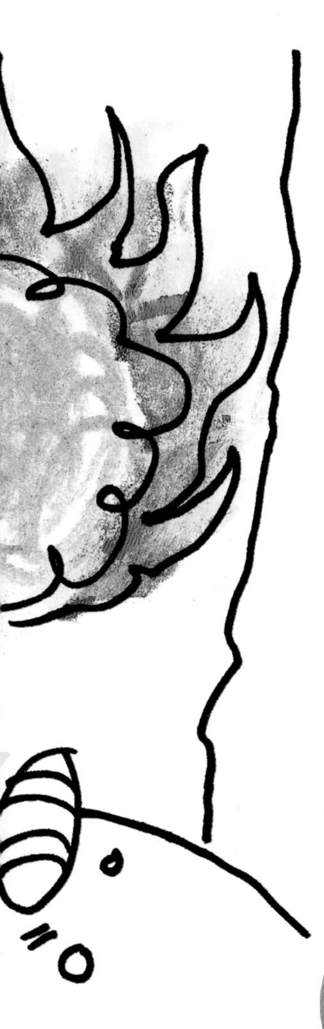

'Whatever's happening in that bush?' Moses murmured.

He wanted to see better, so he took a step closer.

'Stay where you are!' the voice from the bush commanded. 'Take off your shoes. I am the Lord your God. The ground you are standing on is holy.'

Moses could hardly believe his ears.

'How can such an ordinary man be hearing something so EXTRAordinary?' he thought.

'I have an important job for you, Moses,' God continued. 'The king of Egypt is being very unkind to my people, the Israelites. I've chosen YOU to set them free.'

Moses was amazed to hear God speaking to Him.

What is the most extraordinary thing you've ever seen or heard?

Dear Father, thank You that You have chosen me to do important things for You too. Amen.

Moses, a Hero for God

The fire in the bush

Day 13

'But Moses said to God, "I am nobody. How can I ... bring the Israelites out of Egypt?"'
(Exodus 3 v 11)

Moses' mouth dropped wide open.

Moses' eyes grew huge and round.

'I can't set Your people free,' he mumbled. 'I'm nobody. Who's going to take any notice of *me*?'

God answered, 'You won't be on your own. I will be with you. Tell My people that I have sent you to them,' He added. 'Then they will listen to you.'

Moses shook his head. 'But supposing they don't *believe* You sent me?' he frowned. 'Supposing they won't believe You've spoken to me at all?'

Moses thought God was asking too much of him.

Are there things you find difficult? You could ask God to help you with them this week.

Dear God, when I find something hard to do, please help me remember that You are always with me. Amen.

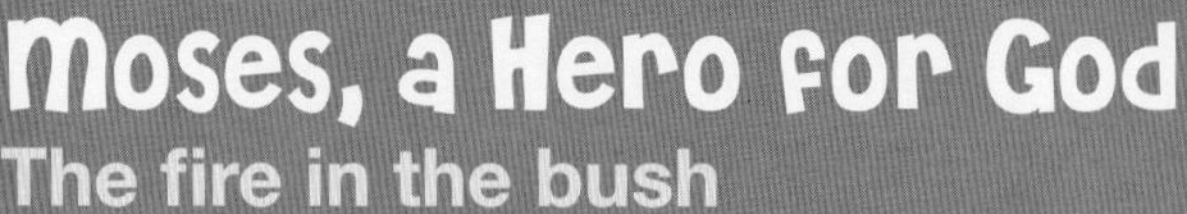

Moses, a Hero for God

The fire in the bush

Day 14

'Do this to prove to the Israelites that the LORD ... has appeared to you.' (Exodus 4 v 5)

Stranger and stranger

God could see that Moses was worried.

'Throw that stick you're holding onto the ground,' He said.

Moses did. Instantly, the stick turned into a snake!

'Aah!' yelled Moses, jumping out of its way.

'Don't be frightened,' God said. 'Now pick up the snake.'

'What?!' Moses gasped fearfully.

But slowly, carefully, he reached out his hand towards the snake. As his fingers touched it, it became a stick again!

'This day gets stranger and stranger,' Moses murmured.

'Show this to My people,' God commanded. 'Then they'll have to believe I've spoken to you.'

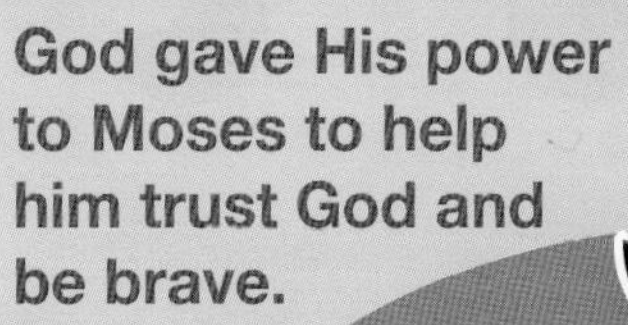

God gave His power to Moses to help him trust God and be brave.

Why are lots of snakes dangerous?

Pens Prayer

You are so powerful, dear God. Teach me to trust You. Amen.

Moses, a Hero for God

The fire in the bush

Day 15

'Now, go! I will help you …' (Exodus 4 v 12)

God's power was huge, but Moses still felt very ordinary.

'I can't go to Egypt,' he muttered. 'I shan't know what to say to people.'

But Moses was the man God had chosen – and Moses was the man God would send.

'You must trust Me,' God replied. 'I will give you the right words to say at the right time.'

Moses still shook his head. 'I'm not sure.'

Then God commanded, 'Take your brother, Aaron, with you. He's good at talking. Now, off you go.'

So off ordinary Moses went to do something EXTRAordinary for God.

Moses was a hero because he learnt to trust God to help him.

What does God want us to do for Him every day?

Pens Prayer

Lord God, here I am. Please help me to be a hero for You. Amen.

Day 16 GROWING UP WITH GOD

'Whoever loves is a child of God and knows God.'
(1 John 4 v 7)

Sunflower charlotte

'… eight, nine, TEN!' Denzil finished counting. 'Coming to find you!'

He was playing hide and seek with Charlotte, who was BRILLIANT at hiding.

Denzil looked under the stairs … behind the sofa … under the table.

Charlotte wasn't there.

'Hum,' Denzil thought. 'She must be upstairs.'

But Charlotte wasn't under the bed … or in the wardrobe … or behind the shower curtain.

At last, Denzil looked out of the window. What was that amongst the tall sunflowers in Charlotte's garden?

'I CAN SEE YOU!' Denzil yelled.

And there Charlotte was, wearing a huge smile that was sunflower-bright.

Being kind when you play with friends pleases God and helps our friendships grow stronger.

Do you have a favourite game you like to play with your friends?

Pens Prayer

Father God, please help me remember how You want me to treat others when I'm doing playful things. Amen.

Day 17 Growing Up with God

'May … God our Father … encourage you and strengthen you always to do and say what is good.' (2 Thessalonians 2 v 16–17)

FLOMP!

When Splodge opened her bedroom cupboard, a big pile of things toppled out.

There were books she didn't look at any more; toys she didn't play with any more; DVDs she didn't watch anymore.

'You need to have a clear-out,' said Squiggle wisely. 'I'll help you.'

Splodge and Squiggle worked away busily.

'Finished at last!' declared Squiggle with a smile.

'Um …' began Splodge. 'That depends what you mean by "finished".'

'The cupboard's tidy,' replied Squiggle.

'Yes,' murmured Splodge, 'but I've just remembered … There are lots of things under my bed as well …'

God is pleased to see us working happily together.

Is there a cupboard or a drawer in your bedroom that needs a good tidy?

Pens Prayer

Lord, I want to be ready to work hard without complaining when it's time to do busy things. Amen.

Day 18 Growing Up with God

'Give thanks to the LORD, because he is good; his love is eternal!' (Psalm 107 v 1)

'Is it time yet?'

Marco was excited.

Too excited to sleep.

Too excited to sit still.

Too excited to do anything.

He was off to stay with his cousin for a few days – and he was travelling by TRAIN!

'I've never been on a train before,' he grinned to Max.

'Have you ever been on a train before?' he beamed to Gloria.

'Is it time to go yet?' he asked Denzil.

At last the moment arrived. Pens waved Marco goodbye.

'He looks so happy,' smiled Gloria. 'Days are wonderful when there's something to be excited about.'

We can share our exciting days with each other and with God.

Have you been on a journey? Where did you go?

Pens Prayer

I praise You, dear Father, for days to do exciting things. Amen.

Day 19 Growing Up with God

'LORD, you have made so many things! How wisely you made them all!' (Psalm 104 v 24)

Pens were out walking.

Not just to the shops, or the park, or each other's houses.

This was a LONG ramble.

'I like rambling,' puffed Denzil, clambering up a steep hill.

'So does Sharpy!' yelled Max, charging down the other side.

'I *love* being out in the country,' smiled Philippa, taking in a deep breath of fresh air.

Denzil stopped to eat a chocolate biscuit.

'Remember to take the wrapper home to put in the bin,' reminded Philippa. 'We mustn't leave litter when we're out and about. God's countryside is beautiful and it's important to look after it.'

God made the world we live in. Let's help to keep it beautiful.

Do you go for walks? Where do you go?

Pens Prayer

Lord God, help me remember to care for Your countryside, so we can all carry on enjoying it. Amen.

Day 20 Growing Up with God

'Do what is right and fair; that pleases the LORD ...'
(Proverbs 21 v 3)

‘Come and see what I’ve got!’ shrieked Charlotte.

She showed Gloria her brand-new kite. It was brightly coloured and light as a feather.

Gloria’s eyes shone. ‘Can I watch it flying?’ she asked.

‘Of course!’ laughed Charlotte. ‘But better than just watching, let’s go and fly it TOGETHER!’

The park was sunny and warm. The sky was brilliant and blue. And the wind was just right for kite-flying!

Up the kite went into the air, dancing and fluttering, dipping and twisting.

‘Wheee!’ cried Gloria excitedly, and her eyes didn’t stop shining all day.

Sharing things with a friend pleases God and can make them twice as much fun!

Who do you sometimes share your toys with? Who sometimes shares their toys with you?

Pens Prayer

Teach me, dear God, to share things with my friends. Amen.

Day 21 Growing Up with God

'... I will give you rest.' (Matthew 11 v 28)

A good book

The Wor

Philippa had had a busy week.

On Monday, she'd cleaned downstairs in her house.

On Tuesday, she'd cleaned upstairs in her house.

On Wednesday she'd done her washing and ironing.

On Thursday she'd tidied up her garden and swept the paths.

On Friday she'd sorted out all her kitchen cupboards and done her shopping.

Then on Saturday Philippa said to herself, 'That's enough busyness for one week. Today I'm going to sit down with a very good book and do absolutely NOTHING AT ALL.'

God knows we need to rest when we've been busy.

Have you been busy this week?

Pens Prayer

Father God, thank You so much for times to rest and be quiet. Amen.

Day 22 Growing Up with God

'I love those who love me; whoever looks for me can find me.' (Proverbs 8 v 17)

The Perfect Place

Squiggle and Splodge were building something secret. They had an old curtain and four long sticks.

Behind that bush! It's the perfect place!

They pushed the sticks a little way into the ground in a square shape. Then they draped the curtain over the top to make four walls and a roof.

'Our very own SECRET den,' chuckled Splodge.

Squiggle smiled, 'I think I'm going to come here and talk to God sometimes. Charlotte says you can talk to God anywhere, but it's fun to have a special place, too.'

'Yes,' Splodge agreed. 'Special *and* secret.'

When we ask Him, God will be with us anywhere and everywhere.

Do you have a playhouse at home or at school or pre-school where you can play with friends?

Pens Prayer

Dear God, thank You for being with me when I'm doing special things. Amen.

Day 23 Growing Up with God

'It is the LORD who gives wisdom; from him come knowledge and understanding.' (Proverbs 2 v 6)

One hundred times

Marco was learning to use a skipping rope.

'I'm going to skip ONE HUNDRED TIMES without stopping,' he said to himself.

He practised and practised, and his skipping got better and better.

He'd just reached thirty skips when Denzil cycled past.

'Hello, Marco!' Denzil shouted.

Marco tripped on the rope.

'Bother,' he puffed. 'Now I'll have to start again.'

Just as he'd counted FIFTY skips, the rope got caught on a bush.

'Nooo!' groaned Marco. 'That means starting again – AGAIN!'

But the next time – he did it! One hundred perfect skips.

'Yesss!' he yelled. 'Marco, the champion skipper!'

God gave us our minds and bodies. Let's use them to learn all we can.

Is there something new you'd like to learn? Who could you ask to help you?

Pens Prayer

Lord, please teach me to be patient and to keep trying when I'm learning things. Amen.

Day 24 Growing Up with God

'I will show you my faith by my actions.' (James 2 v 18)

When Max had a nasty cold, Philippa took Sharpy out for his walks.

When Philippa had toothache, Denzil cut the grass in her garden.

When Denzil hurt his wrist, Charlotte cooked a meal for him.

When Charlotte slipped and banged her head, Marco sat with her until the doctor came.

When Marco had a bad tummy, Gloria cheered him up by telling him stories.

When Gloria was feeling sad, Max and Sharpy invited her to go for a walk along the beach with them.

Pens love helping each other. They really are the very best of friends.

Some of the best days are those spent being kind and helpful.

Have you helped anyone this week? Who could you help tomorrow?

Pens Prayer

Father God, help me to live the way You want me to – showing love to other people and doing helpful things. Amen.

FISHERMEN FRIENDS

Starting the journey with Jesus

Day 25

'[Jesus] saw two boats pulled up on the beach ...' (Luke 5 v 2)

Jesus borrows a boat

Crowds of people were going down to the lake.

Walking. Running. Even skipping.

'Jesus is teaching,' they murmured excitedly.

They all wanted to see Him and hear what He had to say about God.

But because there were so many, there was lots of pushing and shoving. Jesus thought it might be safer to teach everyone from the lake. So He climbed into a boat on the beach. It belonged to a fisherman called Simon Peter.

'I need to go out on the water,' Jesus called. 'If you're not too busy, Simon Peter, perhaps you could take me.'

Wherever Jesus went, crowds of people came to listen to Him.

Can you think of some busy places where there are lots of people?

Pens Prayer

Dear Lord Jesus, thank You for coming so that we can learn more about God. Amen.

Fishermen Friends
Starting the journey with Jesus

Day 26

'Push the boat out further to the deep water ...' (Luke 5 v 4)

Jesus sat in Simon Peter's boat. For a long time, He talked about God to the people by the lake.

When He'd finished teaching, the crowds turned round and went home.

'Now, Simon Peter,' said Jesus, 'let's go fishing.'

Simon Peter shook his head. 'There's no point,' he grumbled. 'We were out all night, but we didn't catch a thing.'

He glanced at Jesus, then at his brother, Andrew, who was in the boat with them. Andrew was a fisherman, too.

'All right,' Simon Peter sighed. 'If You want us to, Jesus, I suppose we can try again.'

Even though Simon Peter was tired, he did as Jesus said.

Do you know the names of some different kinds of fish?

Pens Prayer

Help me to be like Simon Peter, Lord Jesus, and to do as You want me to. Amen.

Fishermen Friends

Starting the journey with Jesus

Day 27

'They ... caught such a large number of fish that the nets were about to break.' (Luke 5 v 6)

Full of fish

Simon Peter and his brother, Andrew, sailed further out onto the lake. Then they dropped their fishing nets in the water.

'We won't catch anything,' Simon Peter thought. 'There's nothing there today.'

Suddenly –

'There's a fish!' Andrew hissed.

'There's another ...' murmured Simon Peter, '... and another, and another!'

If the brothers had looked at Jesus just at that moment, perhaps they would have seen Him smiling.

But they didn't.

They couldn't.

They were too busy trying to pull in the net. It was more full of fish than they'd ever thought possible!

Fishermen like Simon Peter needed to catch plenty of fish to sell to earn money.

When people have fish as pets, what do they keep them in?

Pens Prayer

Thank You, Jesus, that with You wonderful things can happen. Amen.

Fishermen Friends

Starting the journey with Jesus

Day 28

'So they motioned to their partners in the other boat to come and help them.' (Luke 5 v 7)

To the rescue!

Two other fishermen were out in their boat, too.

Simon Peter and Andrew waved at them.

'James! John! Quickly!' they shouted. 'Please come and help us. We can't pull all these fish in by ourselves.'

James and John sailed their boat over as fast as they could. Then the four fishermen heaved on the nets.

Out came the fish from the water.

Into the boats they poured.

Up and down, the boats rocked and swayed.

'We must get back to shore now!' cried Simon Peter. 'There are so many fish, if we don't hurry, we'll sink!'

The four fishermen had never seen such a HUGE catch of fish.

Who should Simon Peter have trusted not to let the boat sink?

Pens Prayer

Dear Jesus, please help me never to forget that You are always beside me. Amen.

Fishermen Friends

Starting the journey with Jesus

Day 29

'When Simon Peter saw what had happened, he fell on his knees before Jesus ...' (Luke 5 v 8)

Jesus is Lord

The four fishermen arrived safely back at the beach – and all they could do was stare. The pile of fish was ENORMOUS!

When Simon Peter had finished gazing at the catch, he began to gaze at Jesus.

The next minute, he was kneeling down in front of Him.

'You must be the Son of God,' he said softly. 'That's the only way You could have helped us catch so many fish.'

Jesus watched Simon Peter thoughtfully.

'What do You want?' the fisherman whispered. 'Why would You help someone like me? I am not a good man.'

Jesus showed God's power to the four fishermen.

How do you think Simon Peter felt when he realised who Jesus was?

Pens Prayer

How AMAZING that the Son of God wants to be MY friend! Thank You, Jesus. Amen.

Fishermen Friends
Starting the journey with Jesus

Day 30

'Don't be afraid; from now on you will be catching people.' (Luke 5 v 10)

The fishermen follow

Jesus smiled at Simon Peter kindly.

'There's nothing to be afraid of,' He said. 'I want you to help me – you and your fishermen friends.

'People need to know who God is.

'People everywhere.

'They need to know that He's real and that He loves them.

'We've caught fish together, Simon Peter,' Jesus grinned. 'Now let's go and catch people and help them make friends with God!'

Jesus turned and began to walk away along the beach.

In less than a moment, the four fishermen were following Him.

Jesus wants US to follow Him and tell other people about God, too.

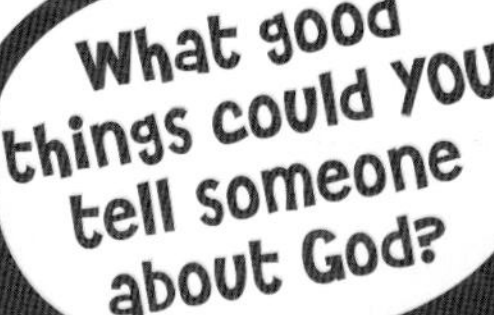

What good things could YOU tell someone about God?

Pens Prayer

Dear Lord Jesus, just like the fishermen, please help me to answer when You call, and follow where You lead. Amen.

Pens titles

More *Pens* for you to enjoy

- ★ Friends
- ★ Father God
- ★ Following Jesus
- ★ Really Special
- ★ Trusting God
- ★ Helping and Serving
- ★ Big and Small
- ★ God's Book
- ★ God's Love
- ★ God Cares
- ★ God's Heroes
- ★ Thank You God

Pens Special! Christmas

The *Pens* characters tell the Christmas story to make Jesus' birth real and memorable for young children, also with five days of Bible-reading notes.

Pens Special! Starting School

Help children start school confidently, knowing that God goes there with them. A short story followed by five days of Bible notes.

Coming January 2012: Pens Special! Easter

For current prices visit **www.cwr.org.uk/store**

Available online, or from your local Christian bookshop.

Published 2011 by CWR, Waverley Abbey House, Waverley Lane, Farnham, Surrey GU9 8EP, UK. Registered Charity No. 294387. Registered Limited Company No. 1990308.

Visit www.cwr.org.uk/distributors for list of National Distributors.

All Scripture references are from the GNB: *Good News Bible* © American Bible Society 1966, 1971, 1976, 1992. Used with permission.

Concept development, editing, design and production by CWR

Printed in China by 1010 Printing Ltd.

ISBN: 978-1-85345-632-9

OTHER CWR DAILY BIBLE-READING NOTES
Every Day with Jesus for adults
Inspiring Women Every Day for women
Lucas on Life Every Day for adults
Cover to Cover Every Day for adults
Mettle for 14- to 18-year-olds
YP's for 11- to 15-year-olds
Topz for 7- to 11-year-olds

Come on in and meet your Pens friends! Together we'll find out how, with God's help, we can be brave and do amazing things for Him that will help our friends get to know God better.
Join us as we draw you closer to God every day through our stories, Bible readings and prayers.
Ideal for children aged 3 to 6
ANTI BEAR SPRAY
HOW TO SURVIVE ANYT

www.cwr.org.uk
ISBN 978-1-85345-632-9
9 781853 456329
Tel: 01252 784700
Email: mail@cwr.org.uk
CWR Applying God's Word *to everyday life and relationships*